FINDING PLACES

HEATH AMERICAN READERS

D.C. Heath and Company
Lexington, Massachusetts / Toronto, Ontario

AUTHORS AND CONSULTANTS

Mildred Bailey

Rose Barragan

Barbara Burke

Barbara B. Cramer

Wilma J. Farmer

Teresa Flores

Charles Hacker

P.J. Hutchins

George Jurata

Nancy Mayeda

Kenneth Smith

Lydia Stack

Mary Wigner

D.C. Heath and Company
Lexington, Massachusetts/Toronto, Ontario

Copyright © 1986, 1983 by D.C. Heath and Company

Printed in the United States of America.

ISBN 0-669-08030-6

3   5   7   9   11   13   14   12   10   8   6   4

Design Credits *Unit Openers:* Thomas Vroman Associates, Inc.

Illustration Credits **14-17:** John Wallner. **18-23:** Tony Rao. **24-29:** Lorna Tomei. **30-35:** Eulala Conner. **38-42:** Fred Harsh. **43-47:** True Kelley. **48-53:** Tien Ho. **54-61:** Jennie Williams. **64-69:** Jerry McDaniel. **70-76:** Jeffrey Terreson. **77-83:** Ronald LeHew. **84-89:** Fieya Tanz. **92-96:** Don Almquist. **97-103:** Susan Lexa. **104-106, 122-127:** Jan Pyk. **107-113:** N. Jo Smith. **116-121:** Steven Schindler (Publishers' Graphics). **128-135:** Paul Blakey. **136-143:** Carol Inouye. **146-152:** Jerry Smath. **153-159, 173-180:** Sal Murdocca. **160-167:** Yee Chen Lin. **168-172:** June Grammer.

Photo Credits **Cover, 1:** Leonard Lee Rue (National Audubon Society Collection/Photo Researchers). **8-9:** Bill Binzen (Image Bank). **10:** Peter Arnold. **11:** Michael Philip Manheim (Photo Researchers). **12:** *t,* Michael Philip Manheim (Photo Researchers); *b,* Yoram Kahana (Peter Arnold, Inc.). **13:** Ginger Chih (Peter Arnold, Inc.). **36-37:** Nilo Lima (Rapho/Photo Researchers). **62-63:** Susan Johns (Rapho/Photo Researchers). **90-91:** Cheryl Walsh (Webb Photos). **114-115:** D. Zirinsky (Photo Researchers). **144-145:** Jeffrey Foxx (Woodfin Camp).

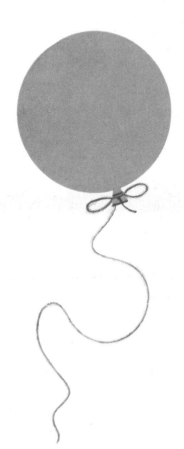

Contents

one

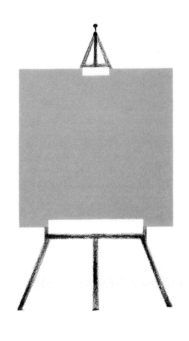

two

three

four

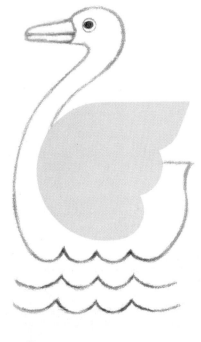

five

six

one

Let's Find

11

12

I Have to Be Me

I can fish in a hat.
I can fish in a pot.
I can fish in a dish,
If I wish. Why not?

I can play and get wet.
And I do it a lot.
If I want, I may play.
But then, I may not.

I can hit with my bat.
And I do it my way.
I can sing when I hit.
I can, and I may.

I can be what I want.
I can do what I do.
I have to be **me**.
And you have to be **you**.

Helping Mike

Fay ran up to Mike and said,
"Come play ball with me."

"I can't," said Mike.
"We plan to go fishing."

"We?" said Fay.

"My father and I," said Mike.

18

"May I go?" said Fay.
"May I please go with you?"

"No," said Mike.
"We plan to go for ten days.
You can't go with us.
But you may help, if you want."

"OK," said Fay. "I will help.
What can I do?"

"Look at all the pots and pans,"
said Mike. "Help me get them in.
Then you can help me get the cot in.
It will be my bed for ten days."

"The pots are in.
The pans are in.
And I am on the cot," said Fay.

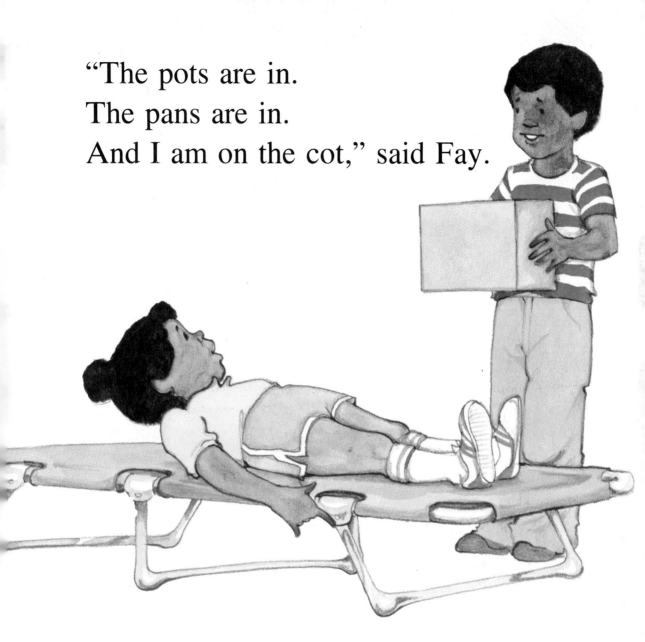

"Get up," said Mike.
"We have to get the cot in.
Then my father and I can go."

"It will not go in," said Fay.

"But it is my bed!" said Mike.
"We have to get it in!"

"It will not fit," said Fay.

"What will I do?" said Mike.
"What will I do with no bed?"

"Look, Mike," said Fay.
"Look at that!
The cot will fit.
You will have a bed."

"That is some bed!"
said Mike.

A Penny to Wish On

Lee was set for bed.

He said, "Please get me a penny."

"A penny?" said Pat. "What for?"

"To wish on," he said.

"I see," said Pat.

Pat got a penny for Lee.

"What are you going to wish for?"
she said.

"Things!" he said. "I can't say
what things. I won't get my wish then."

"OK, I won't ask," said Pat.
"I will go, and then you can wish."

25

"Penny, penny!" said Lee. "Get me out of bed. One, two, three. I wish to be out playing . . . playing. . . ."

Lee was out of bed and in a tree! He was not playing. He was way up in a tree with a Thing.

"Who are you?" Lee said to the Thing.

"Me?" said the Thing. "I can be what you wish. A cat? A dog? A fish? We can hop and play. And we can sing. What do you say, Lee? Will you play with me?"

"No!" Lee said to the Thing.
"Please get me out of the tree!"

"I can't," said the Thing.
"The penny can. Ask the penny."

"Penny, penny!" said Lee. "Please
get me out of the tree. One, two, three.
I wish to be in bed . . . in bed. . . ."

Lee was out of the tree. And he was **out** of bed, not **in** it!

Pat ran to Lee and said,
"Get up, Lee. Get up!
What are you doing?"

"Wishing," said Lee. "And **not** for a penny to wish on!"

The Plan

Ben was sitting down when Peter
said, "Who is going to win, Ben?"

"I am," Ben said. "That is my plan."

"And that is **my** plan," said Peter.

"We will see who wins!" said Ben.

"Yes, we will," said Peter.
"You will try, and I will try."

A man ran up and said,
"OK, get set to go.
The first one to that tree wins."

" I will win!" said Peter.

"No, you won't," said Ben.
" I will win!"

"Come on," the man said. "Get set!
One . . . two . . . three . . . **go!**"

Peter was first. Then Ben was first.

"Out of my way, Ben!" said Peter.

Then the two of them were first!
Peter and Ben ran on and on!

Then . . . Peter was down!

"Oh!" said Peter. "Oh!"

"Are you OK?" said Ben, stopping
to see what was going on.

"No," said Peter. "I have to stop!
But you get going, Ben. Go on!
You can win yet. You have to try!"

"No," said Ben. "I won't go on.
I will sit with you."

Then Ben sat down with Peter.

"I can't go on," Peter said.
"And I was planning to win!"

"Some things you can't plan on,"
Ben said.

"Winning is one of them," said Peter.
" I can see that. One thing
I can plan on, Ben. **You!**
You won't let me down, will you?"

" I will try not to," said Ben.

two

THREE RINGS

"Come on in!" calls the man.
"Come on in. The band is playing.
We have three rings of things.
Not one, not two.
But one, two, three.
Come in and see!"

First the men come out.
Trim men. Slim men.
Men with hats.
Small men. Lots of men.

Then . . . the cats!

See the cats as they sit up.
Can you say which cat is which?

Look up! Look up!
See the men and women
as they go up on the rings.
Look at them fly!

I can't do that. Can you?

They shot that man.
Look at him go!
They shot him to the top.
Has he come down?

Yes, look at him.
He has come down!

Oh, what things to see!
What a day!

SEEDS and WEEDS

"What are they?"
Kay said to Tim.

"Seeds," said Tim.
"When I get them in,
lots of things will come up."

"What is Helen doing?" said Kay.

"She is weeding," Tim said.

Kay ran up to Helen.

"What is weeding?" she said.

"Getting the weeds out," said Helen.

"What is a weed?" said Kay.
"I can't tell which is a weed!"

"See this?" said Helen. "**This** is
a weed. Who needs weeds? No one!"

"Oh, I see," said Kay. "Let me stay and do the weeding with you."

"No, Kay," said Helen.
"Go and ask Tim what to do."

"Do I need to do that?" said Kay.
"Can't I stay with you?"

"Go see him," said Helen.
"Ask him for some of his seeds."

Then Kay said, "I do not need
to see Tim or ask him what to do.
He can have his seeds!
I will get some weeds!
That is what I will do!"

"See?" said Kay to Helen and Tim. "See my weeds?"

"Oh, **no**!" Tim said. "Let me get a pot for you, Kay."

What Will You Be?

"Don," said Lorna. "Look at the things I have. Come and we can play."

"Try one on. Then you will see all the things that you can be," said Lorna.

"This hat looks good for me,"
said Don. "My father can do this.
I will need this pot and pan."

"I will get this off. Then you
can see what it is that **you** will be,"
said Don.

"With this on, I will be a vet,"
said Lorna. "What a good dog.
Do you want him to have his shot?"

"I will get this off. Then you
can see what it is that **you** will be,"
said Lorna.

"With this on, I can get wet,"
said Don. "Let me look for fish
by this weed. I may need my net
to help me."

"I will get this off. Then you
can see what it is that **you** will be,"
said Don.

"With this hat on, I can fly,"
said Lorna. "Will you come
and see me off?"

Get this off and try this on.
Come and play with Lorna and Don.
What things can you be?
Try one on and you will see.

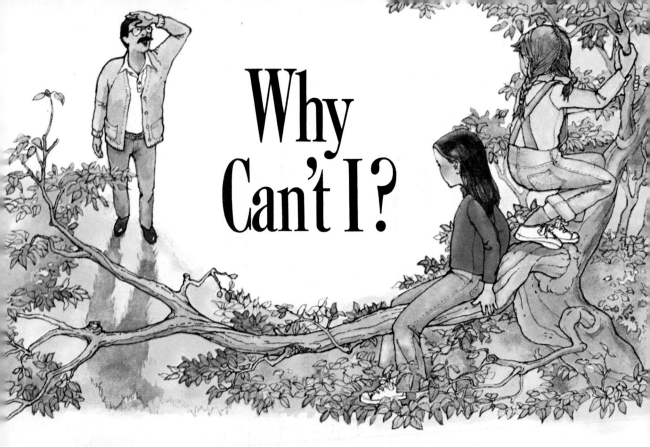

Why Can't I?

Pat and Alice were playing in a tree.

"Pat, we have to go!" her father said.

"Can't I stay with Alice?" said Pat.

"No, Pat," her father said.

Pat got out of the tree,
and so did Alice.

"First let me see Sid," said Pat.
"Then I will go."

"Who is Sid?" said her father.

"That pig in the pen," said Pat.
"I wish Sid were my pet."

"You can have him," said Alice.

"Oh, can I?" said Pat.

"No, you may not," said her father.

"Why not?" said Pat. "Alice says
I can have Sid."

"Yes, Alice did say that,"
said her father. "But I say no.
A pig won't do as a pet.
What will you do with him
when he gets big?"

"Get a big pen for him,"
said Pat. "Alice says a pig has
to stay in a pen."

"**We** can't have a pen!" said her father.

"Please!" said Pat.

"Pat," said her father. "You can have
a cat or a dog! You can't have a pig."

"See? Sid is digging," said Alice.
"Pigs stay in pens and dig."

"Digging!" Pat said. "That won't do!
I can't have a pet that digs!"

"Do you see why Sid has to stay with Alice?" said her father.

"Yes," Pat said. "Sid has to do what pigs do."

"What is that?" said her father.

"Dig!" Pat said. "Dig in a pig pen!"

three

I Can Draw

Joe was drawing a big jet.
Betty was drawing a paw on a cat.

"Say!" Andy said to them.
"You two can draw!"

"Can you draw?" Betty said to Andy.

"No, I can't," Andy said.

"Who says you can't?" said Joe.

"I do," said Andy. "I can't draw the way you and Betty can."

"Why do you feel that way?" said Betty. "You can if you try."

"**No**, I can't draw," Andy said
to them. "I can't!"

"If you feel that way,
then you can't," Joe said.

"Yes," said Betty.
"Let me see you try."

"OK," Andy said. "I will try.
You will see that I can't."

"See what I did?" said Andy.
"I ask you! Is **that** a drawing?"

"You bet it is!" Betty said
when she saw it.

"Yes, it is," Joe said.
"It has a lot in it."

"Oh, come on!" said Andy.

"I do see a lot in that drawing,"
Joe said to Andy. "Why, I see a cat
with his paw in the street."

"And I see a jet flying up,"
said Betty.

"A paw! A street! A jet!" said Andy.
"Why, I **can** draw!
Who says I can't?"

Emma and Leonard did not want
to play. It was a hot, dry day.

"What do you want to do?"
Emma said to Leonard.

"I do not know," said Leonard.

"And I do not know," said Emma.

So the two of them sat and sat.

Then Larry ran by.

"Slow down, Larry," said Leonard.
"Slow down! What are you doing?"

"I am going to get Tom," Larry said.
"Then we are going to a show."

"A show?" Emma said. "What show?"

"You know. The one in the shed,"
said Larry. "Mary is in it.
Do you two want to go with me?"

"No," Emma and Leonard said.

"What a show that is going to be!"
said Leonard. "I bet it will be a mess!"

"I **know** it will!" said Emma.
"I saw one show that Mary was in.
She was in a red dress. And guess what!
A bee was in the shed! When that bee
got on that red dress. . . ."

"Mary ran out!" said Leonard.

"We all ran out," said Emma.
"No show that day!"

Then Jay ran by. "Are you two going
to the show?" he said.

"No, we are not," they said.

Jay ran on, and Emma and Leonard sat.
That show was not for them.

Then Emma said, "I have to go."

"OK, Emma," Leonard said. "See you!"

"I guess so," said Emma.

"What are you doing here?"
said Leonard.

"What are **you** doing here?"
said Emma. "You said this show
was going to be a mess."

"I guess I did," said Leonard.

"Then what are you doing here?"
Emma said.

"Going to the show,"
Leonard said. "And you?"

"Going with you!" said Emma.

The Seesaw

"Lester!" said Sidney. "Come and get on the seesaw with me. Please?"

"What for?" said Lester.

"If you get on, then I will go up," Sidney said.

"OK. I guess so," said Lester.
"I will get on the seesaw."

"Sidney, you did not go up," Lester said.
"Why can't we get off and play tag?"

"No! No!" Sidney said. "I want
to go up and down on the seesaw."

"What do we do next?" said Lester.

"Do not ask me," said Sidney.

Then Flora ran by.

"Flora!" said Sidney.
"Set down that bag and sit
next to Lester. If you do that
for me, I will go up. OK?"

"I guess I can," said Flora,
as she set down her bag.
Then she got next to Lester.

But Sidney did not go up!

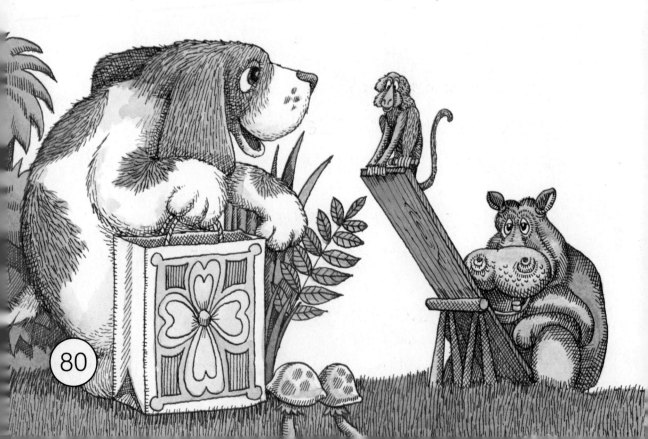

Then Flora saw Betty.
"Betty!" she said. "Get off that stem
and get on the seesaw!"

So Betty got off the stem and sat
in a row next to Flora and Lester.

But Sidney did not go up!

Lester and Flora and Betty sat
in a row. They sat and sat!

"What can we do, Sidney?"
said Betty. "What can we do next?"

"Ask me," said Dan. "Let me get
in the row with you. Then Sidney
will go up."

"If you get on, the seesaw
will sag," said Flora.

"No, it won't sag," Dan said.
Then he got on.

"Up you go, Sidney!" said Lester
and Flora and Betty and Dan.

Look what the seesaw did!

KING

King was a pup when Elizabeth
first got him. He was not a big pup.

"See!" Elizabeth said to Dad.
"He can fit in a big cup!"

"King has big paws," said Dad.
"He will be a big dog. You will have
to show him **what** to do. And you
will have to show him what **not** to do."

84

Elizabeth had a lot of things to do
for King when he was a pup.

First, she had to get her pup
to the vet for shots. That was
the first trip for King.

And the next trip was to get
a dog tag for King.

Elizabeth had to show King
when to sit and when to stay.
Next she had to show King
when to stop and when to go.

Then Elizabeth had to get King wet.
But King did **not** want to get wet.

"Stop, King!" said Elizabeth.
"I am doing this for you! I have
to dry you off, or you will drip.
Then you will slip."

Elizabeth got a bed for King.
"Stay in the bed I got for you,"
Elizabeth said to him.
"Not in my bed!"

But King got up on the bed
with Elizabeth. Then she had
to show King his bed and say,
"Stay, King. Stay!"

Elizabeth said, "King gets up
on beds and things. But I show him
what to do. He knows to do what I ask."

four

What Is That?

Tap! Tap! Tap!
Is that under my bed?
Tap! Tap! Tap!
"Who is tapping?" I said.

Rap! Rap! Rap!
Is that over my bed?
Rap! Rap! Rap!
"Who is rapping?" I said.

Slap! Slap! Slap!
Is it **over** my bed?
Slap! Slap! Slap!
"Is it **under**?" I said.

I will have to get up!
"I can't stay in bed
With tapping and rapping
And slapping!" I said.

So over I go
To get under my bed.
And what do I see?
"Oh, it is **you**!" I said.

"You two are the ones
Who are under my bed!
You are tapping and rapping
And slapping!" I said.

My cat and my pup
Were under my bed.
"Stop slapping that top
And get out!" I said.

The two then got out,
My cat and my pup.
They were slapping that top!
Up and down, down and up!

I said, "That is **that**!"
And got in my bed.
"No tapping, no rapping,
No slapping!" I said.

RAGS and the RUG

"Stop, Rags!" said Jack, as he ran to get his dog. "Stop what you are doing! Do not tug at the rug that way!"

But Rags did not stop.

"What is under that rug? Is it a bug?" Jack said to his pet. "Stop tugging, Rags. Stop it, I say!"

Rags let go of the rug.

"Oh, Rags!" said Jack. "See
what you did to this rug!
Why did you do it?"

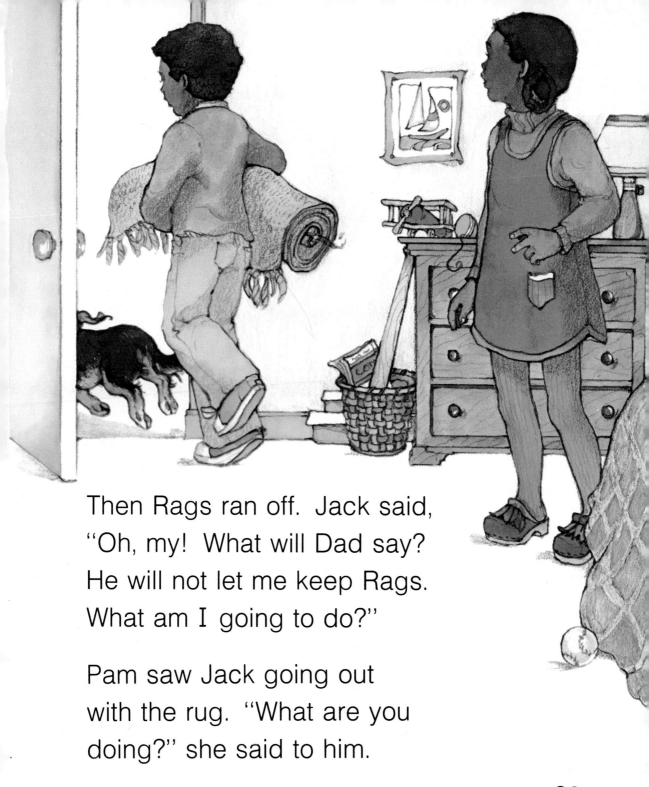

Then Rags ran off. Jack said,
"Oh, my! What will Dad say?
He will not let me keep Rags.
What am I going to do?"

Pam saw Jack going out
with the rug. "What are you
doing?" she said to him.

Jack said, "See what Rags did
to this rug. I will have to fix it."

"Yes," said Pam. "You will have
to show that rug to Dad. And you
will have to fix it."

Jack said to his father, "See this rug?"

"Did you do that to it?" said Dad.
"Or did Rags?"

"It was Rags," Jack said.
"But I did try to stop him.
I will have to fix the rug."

"No," said Dad. "You will
not have to fix it.
But keep trying with Rags.
You can slip up, and so can I.
So why can't Rags slip up?"

Jack and Pam ran to get Rags.

"You see, Jack?" said Pam.
"You can tell things to Dad. He said
you did not have to fix the rug."

"I know," said Jack. "And he
let me keep Rags. I will have
to show that dog what not to do
with rugs. He can sleep on them.
He **can't** tug at them!"

In a Tub

I see three cubs.
I can tell which is which.
They have on three caps.
Cap One, Cap Two, Cap Three.

They step in the tub.
They are going to scrub
As they sit in the tub.
Cub One, Cub Two, Cub Three.

"I will scrub first,"
Says Cub Two to One and Three.
"Oh, no, you won't!"
Says Cub One. "I will scrub first!
First **One**! Then Two, then Three!"

"I will scrub first!
Not you or Cub Two!" says Cub Three.
"We can't keep this up!" says Cub One.
"First **One**, then Two, then Three!"

So who will scrub first?
I say no one will scrub
If they keep on this way!
Not One, not Two, and not Three!

I see three cubs.
They step **out** of the tub!
No scrubbing they do!
Cub One, Cub Two, or Cub Three.

A Street Show

When Connie saw Rob, she said,
"I saw a lot of girls and boys
up the street. What are they doing?"

"Why not go over and ask them?"
said Rob.

So Connie and Rob ran up the street.

When Rob saw Carol, he said, "Say!
What is going on?"

Carol said, "It is a street show."

"Does it have a play in it?" said Rob.

"Yes, it does," said Carol.
"And some girls and boys will sing."

"Have you seen a street show?"
Connie said.

"Not yet," said Rob.

"Then why not stay?" said Connie.

"Come on," Carol said. "You can sit
next to me in the first row."

When they sat down, they saw
Dennis step out.

"What will Dennis do in the show?"
said Connie.

"He will sing," said Carol.

"But he is not singing," said Connie.

Connie ran up to Dennis.
"What is it, Dennis?" she said.

"I can't do it!" said Dennis.
"It is my first show, and I can't sing.
Look at them, Connie! Look at
all the girls and boys!"

"But they are girls and boys
you know," said Connie.

Then Carol and Rob ran up to them.

"You can sing, Dennis," said Rob.

"You have to sing," said Carol.

"I can't sing to them!" said Dennis.

"You will not have to," said Carol.
"Sing to Connie and Rob and me!"

So Dennis did sing. He did not sing
to all the boys and girls. But he did sing
to Connie and Carol and Rob.

five

Rabbit and the Doll

Rabbit had some weeds.

"I do not want weeds," Rabbit said.
"I want good things."

Donna and Ken had good things.
Rabbit saw the good things on stalks.

"Well, I will get that," said Rabbit.

Donna and Ken go.

"I will run," said Rabbit.
"I will run and get the good things."

Rabbit ran to the stalks.
Rabbit got some good things.

"Well, this is fun!" said Rabbit.
"It is fun to have good things!"

Donna and Ken saw the stalks.
"What did this?" said Ken.
"We need to stop it!"

"I have a plan!" said Donna.
"First I will run and get my doll."

Donna got her doll.
"See what I do to the doll," said Donna.
Next, she set the doll in the stalks.

Rabbit saw the doll.
"Who are you?" Rabbit said.

The doll did not talk.

"Can't you talk?" said Rabbit.
"Who are you? Talk to me!"

The doll did not talk.

"Can't you walk or talk?" said Rabbit.

The doll did not walk or talk.

Rabbit set his paws on the doll.
His paws did not come off.

"Help!" said Rabbit.
"Let go of me! I can't walk!
This is not fun!"

The doll fell down.
Rabbit fell down with the doll.

"Look!" Ken said.
Donna and Ken saw Rabbit.
Rabbit had his paws on the doll.

"Well, my plan was good,"
said Donna. They let Rabbit go.
"Get out of here!" Donna said.

Rabbit ran off.
"I'll stay in the weeds," he said.
"That doll is not good!"

Ways to Know Things

This is a way to know things.

Do you know what this is?

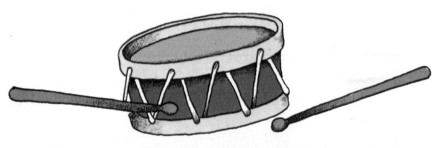

You say it is a drum.
Raps and taps can tell you
that this is a drum.

If you do not see some things,
you can tell what they are.

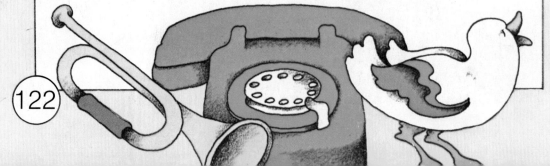

You can tell what things are
by feeling them. I can not see
my ribs, but I can feel them.
You have ribs. Try feeling them.

Here are some things. What can
you tell by feeling them?

Here are ribs. I bet you know
what to do with them. That is
a good way to know things. But
it may be a mess. You may need
a bib for this. A bib will help
if the ribs drip!

If you do not see some things,
can you guess what they are?

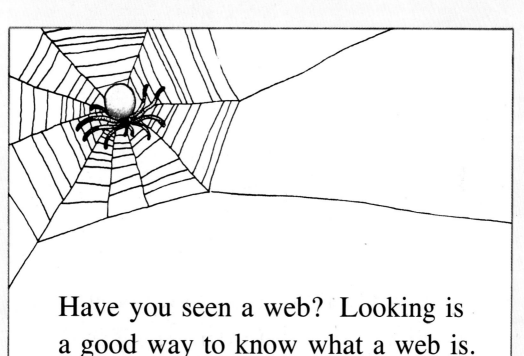

Have you seen a web? Looking is
a good way to know what a web is.
This bug does not want you to feel
her web. Can you guess why?

Here are things that are good
to look at. Do not feel them.
Can you tell why?

Some things are fun to get
to know this way.

Some are not. Can you tell which
is which?

Here are some ways to know things.
Try them all today!

In the Tent

Walter and Leo had wished for a tent.
They had asked and asked for it.

Then one day, Mother said, "Here is
the tent you wanted. We spent a lot
for it! You may sleep in it. Have fun!"

So Walter and Leo went to sleep
in the tent.

"Did we bring the things we need?"
asked Walter.

"Yes," said Leo.

Then Walter said, "It is so still!"

"Do you want to talk?" asked Leo.

So the two of them talked and talked.

Then Leo said, "Well, we have
to get some sleep."

So in the still, still tent
they went to sleep.

Walter sat up. "Leo! **Leo**!"
he said. "Get up!"

"What is it?" said Leo.

"See that!" Walter said.

"Yes," Leo said. "It is walking.
Here it comes! I am getting out!"

131

"I am going with you!"
said Walter.

"Stay next to me,"
Leo said.
"And you will be OK."

So the two of them
ran to a tree.

"See **that**!" Leo said.
"It went **in** the tent!
I will call out and
see who it is."

Leo called, "Who is it?"

"**Me**!" it said.

"It can talk!" said Leo.
"Come on! We will go
in the tent and
see who it is."

When they went in the tent,
they saw Mother.

"Why, Mother!" Leo said.
"What are you doing in the tent?"

"Here is some cake for you,"
said Mother.

"Cake!" said Walter.

"Good!" said Leo.

Mother looked at them. "When I walked to the tent, you ran out," she said. "Why?"

Walter and Leo did not tell her why they ran. All they said was, "Staying in a tent is lots of fun!"

What Do You Need?

Rosa wanted a dog. She wanted the dog that Ruth had in her pet shop. One day, Rosa went to the pet shop with her drum.

"Will you let me have the dog
with the big spots?" Rosa asked.
"Then I will let you have this drum."

"I can't let you have a dog for a drum,"
said Ruth. "I do not need a drum."

"What do you need?" asked Rosa.

"I need a fish for my shop,"
said Ruth. "Bring me a fish,
and I will let you have the dog."

Rosa went to get a fish for Ruth.
On the way, she saw Mike. He had
a small fish that he did not need.

"Let me have that fish," said Rosa.
"Then I will let you have this drum."

"I need a net, not a drum,"
said Mike. "Bring me a net. Then
I will let you have the fish."

Rosa went to get a net for Mike.
On the way, she saw Dan. He had
a net that he did not need.

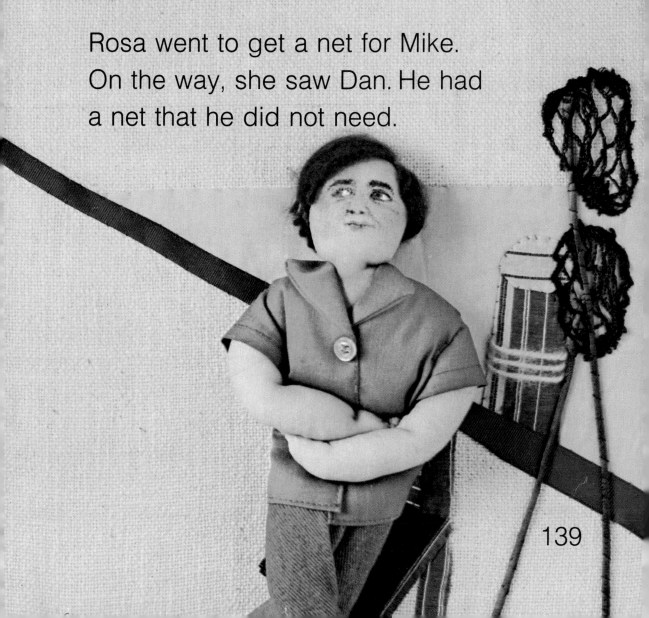

"Let me have that net," said Rosa.
"Then I will let you have this drum."

"I need a pot, not a drum,"
said Dan. "Bring me a pot, and you
can have the net."

Rosa went to get a pot for Dan.
On the way, she saw Carla. Carla
was hitting a pot.

"You seem to need a drum,"
said Rosa.

"Yes, I do," said Carla.
"This pot is not a good drum."

"Let me have that pot," said Rosa.
"And I will let you have this drum."

"You can have the pot," said Carla.
"A drum is what I need."

Rosa let Carla have the drum.
Carla let Rosa have the pot.
Rosa let Dan have the pot,
and Rosa got the net.

Next, Rosa let Mike have the net
and got the fish. Then Rosa let Ruth
have the fish, and Rosa got the dog
with the spots!

six

This is it!

"What are you doing, Pam?"
Dave asked. "What is that mess?
What did you spill?"

"What mess?" asked Pam.
"Stay and you will see
what I am going to make."

"Well, it looks as if you spilled
things!" said Dave. "But I will stay
to see what you are going to make."

"Well, Dave," said Pam. "This is it!"

"What **is** it?" Dave asked her.

"It is my car. It is my star car,"
said Pam.

"A star car!" said Dave.
"Why did you make that car?"

"Well, Dave," Pam said. "That car
is going to take me up to the stars."

"Come on," said Dave.
"Will that car go up?
Will it take you up to the stars?"

148

"Yes, it will go up!" Pam said.

"Well, it won't!" said Dave.
"It won't take you that far."

"Is that **so**!" Pam said.
"I do not want to brag.
But my star car will go up!"

"The stars are so far up," Dave said.
"That thing will not take you."

"Well, I know it will!" said Pam.

"I say you are bragging!" Dave said.

"And I say I am not bragging!"
said Pam. "I will show you!"

"Get in and show me then," said Dave.
"I want to see you take off!"

"I am on my way!" said Pam, stepping in.
"First I get it to hum. Hum! Hum!
Next, brake off! All set for **go**!"

And then Pop! Pop! Pop!

"Pam, are you OK?" Dave asked.

"I seem to be," said Pam.
"But I did not go far.
And I did not get to the stars."

Get Smart!

Up and down went Buster!
"Oh! Oh!" he said. "I can't do it!"

"Keep going, Buster," said Ben. He
was sitting under a tree in the shade.
"You know you want to take off some
of that fat. You do not want to drag
from tree to tree!"

"I know!" Buster said. "But I can't
go on! It is so hot!"

"Yes, it is hot!" Ben said.
"But do you want to keep dragging
from tree to tree?"

"**No**!" said Buster.

"Well," Ben said. "To slim down,
you have to start some way."

"Take it from me," said Buster.
"This is no way to start!"

"Come over in the shade then,"
said Ben. "And keep going!"

So up and down, up and down
went Buster in the shade. "Say!"
he said to Ben. "You have jam!
Let me have some?"

"I will not!" said Ben.
"Jam is what made you fat!"

"I know it," said Buster.
"But I still want some."

As Buster and Ben were talking,
Donna walked by. She had some cake.

Buster called to her, "Oh, Donna!
May I have some cake?"

"You may have part of it," she said.

156

"**No**!" said Ben, running to stop her.
"Can't you see that Buster is trying
to slim down? No cake for him!"

"A **small** part?" asked Buster.

"No," said Donna. "Get smart, Buster.
Keep trying to slim down."

Up and down went Buster
as Donna and Ben talked in the shade.

Then Ted walked by. Buster
called out to him, "Oh, Ted!
Do you have some candy?
Let me trade part of my bag
for part of what you have."

"Buster, **you** have candy!" said Ben
and Donna. "Oh, no!"

"Well, I try to slim down," said Buster.
"But I need my candy!"

"Get smart, Buster!" said Ben.
"You know candy made you fat.
You can't keep dragging from tree
to tree. You have to slim down!"

"I know it," Buster said.
"But I will keep this candy.
It won't make me fat!"

"**What**!" they all said.

"It won't make me fat if I keep it
in the bag," said Buster.

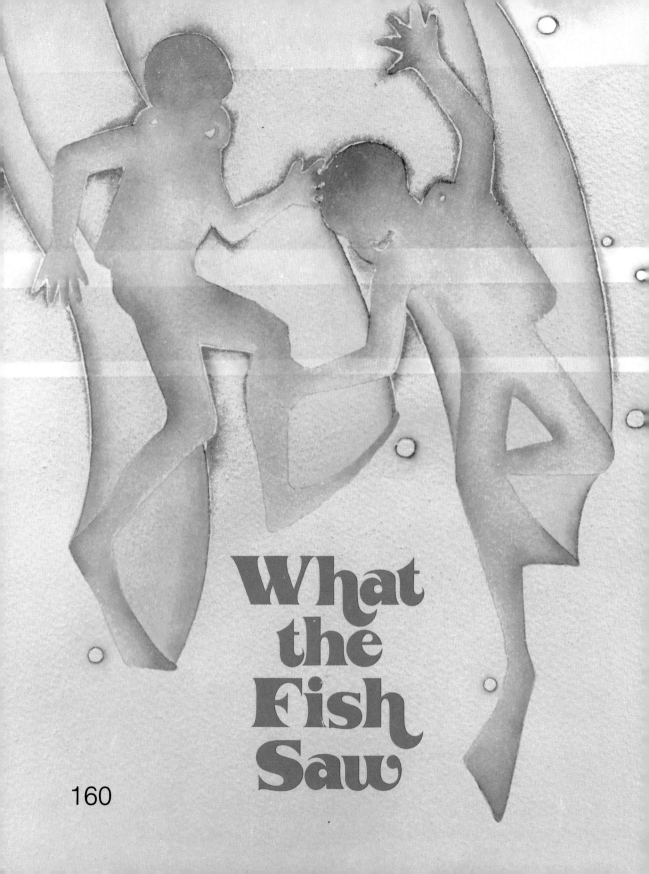

What the Fish Saw

"What are they, Mother?" asked the small fish. "Did you see them go past? They do not go as fast as fish do."

"No, they can't go as fast," said the mother fish. "They are a boy and a girl. They come from dry land to this wet land."

"What are they doing here?"
asked the small fish.

"I do not know. But on the last trip,
they seemed to be looking for fish,"
said the mother.

"Maybe the boy and girl are looking
for the fish they saw on the last trip,"
said the small fish.

"Look! The girl is going into the weeds," said the small fish. "It is dark in the weeds."

"Yes," said his mother. "You can't see the sun over by the weeds. The girl is under the weeds in the shade."

"The girl sees a big thing under the weeds," said the small fish. "Look at her go into the dark spot under the weeds."

"The girl can't go as fast down here
as she can on dry land,"
said the mother fish. "Maybe
she is dragging the big thing
as fast as she can."

"The boy has come to see
what is under the weeds,"
said the small fish. "I want
to see what it is!"

"Look! Is that a penny in his hand?"
the small fish asked.

"Yes, it is a penny," said the mother.
"Far in the past, that thing fell
down here. It was from the dry land,
far from here."

"Mother, the boy and girl can't stand
still. They are hopping up and down.
I guess it was a good penny
from the past," said the small fish.

"Why are the boy and girl going?"
asked the small fish. "Why are
they going up?"

"They are not fish," said the mother.
"They can't stay down here.
The boy needs to stand on dry land.
The girl needs to feel the hot sun
on her hands and face."

"I know," said the small fish.
"And I bet they want to show
what they got down here!"

A SMART PUP

Patty showed Fred her small dog.
She said, "I got a pup today."

"May I pet him?" asked Fred.

"First let him smell you," said Patty.

"See!" said Fred. "He is smelling
my hand. He will let me pet him!"

"Arf! Arf!" said the pup.

"Do not bark!" Patty said.
"Do not bark when Fred pets you!"

"You can't blame him for barking.
A pup has to bark," Fred said.
"Can he play ball?"

"Look," Patty said. "He is bringing
me the ball. He wants to play."

"Is that all he can do?" asked Fred.

"No, he is smart," Patty said.
"He is so smart he can talk!"

"Then make him talk!" Fred said.

So Patty said to the pup, "Talk!"

"Arf! Arf! Arf!" said the smart pup.

"That is not the same as talking,"
said Fred. "That is barking!"

"Well, that is dog talk," said Patty.

Fred said, "Does this dog have a name?"

"Not yet," said Patty. "I am to blame."

"Maybe we can name him," said Fred.
"See that mark on him? That dark spot?
Maybe we can call him Mark."

"That is it," said Patty. "His name
will be Mark!"

Then the pup saw the mark!

"See what he is doing?" Fred said.
"He is getting that mark off.
He does not look the same."

"My, he got that mark off fast!"
said Patty. "I know a name for him."

"What is it?" asked Fred.

"Spark!" said Patty. "He is as fast
as a spark."

A BIG MESS

"It is a big mess, I guess," said Alice.

"Tim says you are to blame," said Ted.

"I can fix it today. I will talk to Tim," said Alice.

"Stay away from him. He will not talk to you," Ted said. "He says you are to blame."

"But I can fix the mess. He will see that I can," said Alice.

"I will talk to him first," said Ted. "I will tell him you can."

"OK, you go first. Then I will come," said Alice.

"You sit here," said Ted. "I will tell Tim you are not to blame. You can come next."

So Ted went out, but Alice did not
sit still.

"I know what I did," said Alice.
"I will talk to Tim. I will tell him.
I can fix the mess fast."

And Alice went to look for Tim.

On the street, Alice started to run.
She slowed down when she saw Ted.
Ted did not see her, but he did see Tim.

Tim was standing in the shade under a
tree. The sun was hot. His face was red.
Was it the sun that made his face red?

Alice looked at Tim. "I know why
his face is red," she said.

"Here I am," said Ted to Tim.
"I have come to talk to you."

"I can guess why," said Tim.

"Why?" said Ted.

"Alice!" said Tim.

"Yes," said Ted.

"Keep her far from me," said Tim.
"She has made a mess!"

Then Alice walked over to them.

"Keep her out of my way, or I will go!" Tim said.

"Please talk to her," said Ted.

"You made a big mess, Alice," said Tim. He started to go. Then he stopped and looked at Alice.

178

"Alice, do you know who was here?" said Tim. "Pam and Pat and Carol and Ken. Helen and Jack and Connie and Kay. They all wanted to see the show. But you did not come, so we had no show. You did not bring Rags or Ribs."

"Well, Rags and Ribs went to the vet," said Alice. "They had shots. But I can bring them today. Today they can be in the show!"

"Can they, Alice?" asked Tim.
"Your dogs are smart. If they
can come, we can have a show today."

"We can tell Pam and Pat and Carol
and Ken," said Ted. "Helen and Jack
and Connie and Kay will want to come."

"Rags and Ribs can come with us
to tell them," said Alice.

"This will be fun," said Tim.
"Smart dogs can do a good show."

New Words

The following words are introduced in *Finding Places.* Each is listed beside the number of the page on which it appears for the first time. The words printed in black are developmental words, and those printed in blue are new words that pupils can decode independently.

Only base forms are given. Note, however, that the skill of doubling the final consonant before adding *-ing* to a verb form is developed in selection 5. Adding *-ed* to a verb form without a base change is developed in selection 20.

Selection 2
14. hat
    if
16. bat

Selection 3
18. can't
    father
    Fay
    plan
    ran
20. cot
    pan
    them

Selection 4
24. Lee
    Pat
    penny
    see

25. ask
    won't
26. three
    tree

Selection 5
30. Peter
31. first
    man
33. oh

Selection 6
38. band
39. slim
    trim
40. as
    they
    which

41. women
42. has

Selection 7
43. Helen
    Kay
    seed
    Tim
    weed
44. need
    tell
    this
45. his
    stay
46. or

Selection 8
48. Don
    Lorna
49. off

Selection 9
54. Alice
    did
55. Sid
56. says
57. big
60. dig

Selection 10
64. Betty
    draw
    jet
    Joe
    paw
65. feel
67. drawing
    saw
68. street

Selection 11
70. dry
    Emma
    know
    Leonard
    show
71. Larry
    slow
    Tom
72. Mary
    mess
73. bee
    dress
    guess
    red
74. Jay
75. here

Selection 12
77. Lester
    seesaw
    Sidney
78. tag
79. next
80. bag
    Flora

81. row
    stem
83. sag

Selection 13
84. cup
    Dad
    Elizabeth
    King
    pup
85. had
    trip
87. drip
    slip
89. today

Selection 14
92. over
    rap
    tap
    under
93. slap

Selection 15
97. bug
   Jack
   Rags
   rug
   tug
99. keep
   Pam
100. fix
103. sleep

Selection 16
104. cap
   cub
   scrub
   step
   tub

Selection 17
107. Connie
   Rob
108. Carol
   does

109. seen
110. Dennis

Selection 18
116. Donna
   Ken
   stalk
   well
117. fun
   run
118. doll
119. talk
   walk
120. fell

Selection 19
122. drum
123. rib
124. bib
125. web

Selection 20
128. Leo
   Mother
   spent
   tent
   Walter

129. bring
   still
   went
134. cake

Selection 21
137. spot
141. seem

Selection 22
146. Dave
   make
   spill
147. car
   star
148. take
149. brag
   far
151. brake
   hum
152. pop

183

Selection 23

153. Buster

drag

from

shade

smart

154. start

155. jam

made

156. part

158. Ted

trade

Selection 24

161. fast

land

past

162. last

maybe

163. dark

into

sun

165. hand

stand

166. face

Selection 25

168. Fred

smell

169. arf

bark

blame

170. same

171. mark

name

172. spark